The children went to an adventure park. They were excited.

They all wanted to go on the Treetop
Adventure.

"This looks exciting," said Chip.

Chip put on a harness. The harness
had a clip at the front.

Chip went across the log bridge.
"Come on, Biff," he called. "You can't
fall off."

Biff began to go across the bridge.
"This is exciting," she said.

Kipper went on the rope runway.
"Off you go!" said Mum.

"Here I come," called Kipper. He went down fast.
"I want to go next," said Biff.

Biff and Dad went in a red canoe.
"Come on!" called Biff. "You won't
fall in!"

Mum, Chip and Kipper went in a green canoe.

They went across the lake. It was fun
in the canoes.

Chip saw a big bird in the sky.
"Look at that big bird," he said.
"What do you think it is?"

It was time for a barbecue. They all
helped to bring the food. Dad lit the
barbecue.

"I am hungry," said Kipper.
"It won't be long," said Dad.

They all sat at the table. Dad was
busy. There was a lot to cook.

"This looks good," said Dad. "Look
at this chicken leg! What a good
cook I am!"

A big bird swooped down. It had
straps on its legs. It took the chicken
leg from Dad's hand.

The bird flew back into a tree. It began to eat the chicken leg.

The bird sat in the tree. Everyone
looked up at it.
"It must be hungry," said Biff.

Dad got his mobile phone.
"A bird has escaped," he said.

A woman came to catch the bird. It flew down and landed on her arm.

"This bird is called a falcon," said the woman.

"It took Dad's chicken leg!" said Biff.

The woman took the <u>falcon</u> home.
Everyone went with her.

They looked at all the birds.
"What beautiful birds," said Chip.

They went back but the chicken legs
were burnt.
"I'm still hungry!" said Kipper.